AMULET

AMULET

Kazu Kibuishi

BOOK TWO
THE STONEKEEPER'S CURSE

AN IMPRINT OF

■SCHOLASTIC

NEW YORK TORONTO LONDON AUCKLAND SYDNEY MEXICO CITY NEW DELHI HONG KONG

LET GO OF ME. I DON'T WANT TO SEE HIM!

YOU BETTER START BEHAVING, BOY. YOUR FATHER WILL HURT YOU WORSE THAN US, I SWEAR TO YOU.

AND I, FOR ONE, HOPE HE DOES.

JUST REMEMBER WHO YOU'RE TALKING TO, SERVANT.

THWOK!

THERE. THAT SHOULD DO IT, NAVIN.

PSSSHT!

HOW'S IT GOING OVER THERE?

I GOT IT SECURED, COGSLEY.

GOOD WORK, KID. NOW LET'S GET THIS THING MOVING.

YOU TAKE THE DRIVER'S SEAT AND I'LL SHOW YOU HOW TO PILOT THE HOUSE.

REALLY?

IF FOR SOME REASON I'M DISABLED, THEN I EXPECT YOU TO TAKE THE CONTROLS.

YOU'RE MY INSURANCE POLICY, GOT IT?

GOT IT.

I HOPE EVERYONE LIKES THEIR EGGS SCRAMBLED.

THEODORE -- TAKE THIS TO CAPTAIN EMILY.

AND TELL HER WE'LL BE ARRIVING IN KANALIS SHORTLY.

YES, SIR.

KLAK!

WE WILL BE ARRIVING IN KANALIS SOON.

THANK YOU, THEODORE.

HMM.

WHAT IS IT, MORRIE?

IT APPEARS YOUR MOTHER'S CONDITION IS WORSE.

THE POISON IS GROWING EVEN STRONGER.

CAN'T WE DO ANYTHING TO SLOW IT DOWN?

I'VE TRIED EVERYTHING.

BUT THE POISON IS TOO POWERFUL FOR THE MEDICINES WE HAVE HERE.

I JUST HOPE THE DOCTORS IN KANALIS HAVE SOMETHING.

THERE IS ONE MORE THING THAT'S BEEN BOTHERING ME.

THIS WHOLE TIME, WHILE WORKING IN HERE, I'VE HAD THIS... STRANGE FEELING.

FEELING?

IT'S... UNSETTLING,

LIKE THERE'S SOMEONE ELSE IN THIS ROOM BESIDES THE THREE OF US.

YOU DON'T SENSE IT?

NO. NO, I DON'T.

I-I'M SORRY.

I SHOULD GO HELP THE OTHERS PREPARE FOR OUR ARRIVAL IN KANALIS.

LET ME KNOW IF YOU NEED ANYTHING.

HWEEEEE

THEY'RE COMING.

WHO IS?

WE SHOULD HAVE DESTROYED THE ELF PRINCE WHEN WE HAD THE CHANCE.

NOW THEY WILL STOP AT NOTHING TO KILL YOU.

WHY WOULD THEY WANT TO KILL ME?

BY NOT JOINING THEM, YOU HAVE BECOME THEIR SWORN ENEMY. YOU ARE SIMPLY TOO POWERFUL FOR THEM TO LEAVE YOU ALONE.

YOU MUST PREPARE FOR BATTLE.

BATTLE? WHAT BATTLE?

HWEEEE...

SHOULD WE ATTACK THEM NOW, SIR?

NOT YET.

HAVE SOMEONE FOLLOW THEM.

WE WILL NEED TO SEPARATE THEM FROM THEIR HOUSE IN ORDER TO TAKE IT OVER.

NOW WATCH CAREFULLY, TRELLIS.

I'M GOING TO SHOW YOU HOW TO EARN YOUR FATHER'S TRUST.

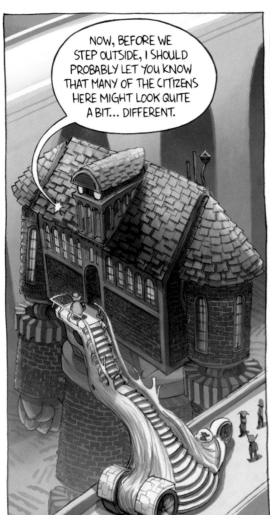

NOW, BEFORE WE STEP OUTSIDE, I SHOULD PROBABLY LET YOU KNOW THAT MANY OF THE CITIZENS HERE MIGHT LOOK QUITE A BIT... DIFFERENT.

DIFFERENT? WHAT DO YOU MEAN, MISKIT?

JUST DON'T STARE AT THEM.

FWOOOOSH!

I HAVE THEM IN MY SIGHTS, SIR.

GOOD.

STRIKE SWIFTLY AND SILENTLY.

THE CHILDREN ARE PRIORITY ONE.

YES, SIR.

THEY WON'T EVEN KNOW WHAT HIT THEM.

WHAT ARE YOU DOING!? GET OUT OF MY WAY!!

HUH?

I SAID, GET OUT OF MY--

WAY!!

SHH.

MAYBE WE SHOULD ASK SOMEONE, MISKIT.

DO NOT WORRY, MISS EMILY.

I KNOW MY WAY AROUND HERE.

WHAT ARE THOSE PEOPLE WAITING FOR?

THEY'RE IN LINE FOR THE SOUP KITCHEN.

HMM.

I DON'T REMEMBER SEEING SO MANY HUNGRY BEFORE.

IT JUST TAKES A LITTLE PATIENCE.

GRRR.

POW!!!

OOF!

ERRRR..

I TOLD YOU TO MIND YOUR OWN BUSINESS.

NNNGH.

WELCOME, DEARS!

MAY I HELP YOU WITH SOMETHING?

WE NEED TO SEE A DOCTOR.

WELL, I'D SAY YOU'VE COME TO THE RIGHT PLACE THEN!

PLEASE FOLLOW ME.

ARACHNOPODS ARE HIGHLY TOXIC.

MOST CASES RESULT IN DEATH.

SHE'S LUCKY TO STILL BE ALIVE!

CAN YOU HELP HER?

ONLY THE FRUIT OF A GADOBA TREE CAN FIGHT THE VENOM AND CURE HER.

DO YOU KNOW WHERE I CAN FIND ONE?

THE LAST REMAINING TREES STAND AT THE PEAK OF DEMON'S HEAD MOUNTAIN...

BUT EVEN THE ELVES WON'T GO THERE.

MANY ELVES SET OUT IN SEARCH OF THE HEALING GADOBA FRUITS. THE ELF KING WOULD ORDER HIS MEN TO REGULARLY CLIMB TO THE SUMMIT. AND OF THE HUNDREDS SENT --

-- NONE HAVE RETURNED.

I CAN'T LET YOU GO THERE IN GOOD CONSCIENCE.

IT'S FAR TOO DANGEROUS.

HEY, GUYS?

I DON'T THINK GOING THERE'S A GOOD IDEA.

I'M HERE FOR ONLY ONE REASON, AND THAT'S TO GET MY FAMILY HOME SAFE.

IF THAT MEANS WE HAVE TO CLIMB A MOUNTAIN, THEN THAT'S WHAT WE'RE GOING TO DO.

IS THAT REALLY THE ONLY REASON?

YOU'RE NOT A BOUNTY HUNTER.

WHO ARE YOU?

...OR DID SILAS FORGET TO TEACH YOU ABOUT YOUR INHERITANCE, STONEKEEPER?

MY NAME IS LEON REDBEARD.

I'M NOT LOOKING FOR PAY OF ANY KIND.

I ONLY ASK THAT YOU ALLOW ME TO TRAVEL WITH YOU AND FIGHT BY YOUR SIDE.

MY MASTER LEFT ME WITH THE DUTY OF PROTECTING EMILY FROM PEOPLE LIKE YOU.

PEOPLE LIKE ME?

DO YOU HAVE ANY IDEA WHAT YOU'RE UP AGAINST?

RING RING!

IS EVERYONE HERE?

I'M GOING TO DO A COMPLETE SHUTDOWN SO THE ELVES CAN'T GET ANY INFORMATION.

BUT THAT MEANS WE'LL BE FULLY OUT OF COMMISSION, UNDERSTAND?

IT'LL BE UP TO YOU TO TURN US BACK ON.

AND YOU BETTER GET HERE BEFORE THEY TURN US INTO SCRAP METAL!

I'M COUNTIN' ON YOU, BUDDY!

READY?

CLICK!

BZAK!

SZT!

LOOK, YOU'RE GOING TO NEED MY HELP.

WHETHER YOU LIKE IT OR NOT.

45

IS THERE AN UNDERGROUND EXIT HERE?

WE HAVE AN EMERGENCY RAIL SYSTEM THAT RUNS THROUGH THE CITY'S ABANDONED MINE SHAFTS.

IT LEADS TO A SAFE HOUSE.

SEND ALL YOUR PATIENTS AND STAFF TO THE ESCAPE ROUTE NOW.

EVERYONE?

WAIT, WHY ARE WE TAKING THE PATIENTS WITH US?

BECAUSE THE ELVES ARE ALREADY HERE.

CHOOM!!!

WHAT WAS THAT?

WE HAVE TO LEAVE.

NOW.

EVERYONE, THIS WAY!

DOWNSTAIRS, QUICKLY!

WATCH YOUR STEP!

THIS
WAY.

THE COAST
IS CLEAR.

THE ELVES
TOOK OVER
THE STREETS.

WHAT DO
WE DO
NOW?

WE TAKE
THE HIGH
ROAD.

WHAT ARE YOU WAITING FOR?

ARE YOU KIDDING?! WE CAN'T DO THAT!

THIS IS WHY YOU SHOULDN'T HAVE TAGGED ALONG!

YOU CAN'T, BUT SHE CAN.

I DON'T KNOW HOW.

SHE DOESN'T KNOW HOW!!

YES SHE DOES.

NOW STOP FOOLING AROUND DOWN THERE OR YOU'RE GOING TO GET US KILLED!

GET ON MY BACK.

DON'T LET HIM BULLY YOU.

C'MON.

YOU SURE ABOUT THIS, EMILY?

VERY GOOD!

NOW TRY AND KEEP UP WITH ME!

HE HAS TO BE JOKING.

THERE'S NO SIGN OF THEM ANYWHERE, SIR.

THEN YOU'RE NOT LOOKING HARD ENOUGH.

IS THIS WHAT YOU WANTED TO SHOW ME?

PATIENCE, WE ARE ONLY GETTING WARMED UP.

BEEP BEEP!

WHAT IS IT?

WE'VE SPOTTED THEM, SIR.

THEY'RE UP ON THE ROOFTOPS.

DESTROY THEM.

LOOK OUT, GUYS!

WE'VE GOT COMPANY!

CLASP!

ERRGH!

SO EASY, ISN'T IT?

SO EASY TO HAVE SO MUCH POWER.

GET OUT...

OF...

...MY HEAD!

EMILY!

UNH!

OOF!!

EMILY!

EMILY, GET UP!

UNNH...

GET IT OFF OF ME!!!

WHY CAN'T I GET THIS STUPID THING OFF?!

IT IS YOUR CURSE.

I'M SORRY IT HAS COME DOWN TO YOU, EMILY,

BUT IT IS YOUR CHOSEN PATH.

YOU HAVE YET TO UNDERSTAND THE EXTENT OF YOUR POWER,

BUT WHEN YOU DO, AND YOU LEARN TO CONTROL IT, I HAVE FAITH THAT YOU WILL TURN THIS CURSE INTO A BLESSING FOR YOU AND ALLEDIA.

YES. HE'S FOUND THE NEW STONEKEEPER, BALAN.

HE'S FOUND THE FIFTH MEMBER OF THE COUNCIL!

AFTER ALL THESE YEARS OF SEARCHING, HE FINALLY FOUND HIM --

FOUND HER.

SHE IS A YOUNG WOMAN.

AND THIS IS HER FAMILY.

HELLO.

THEY ARE SILAS'S DESCENDANTS!

THEN IT'S JUST AS THE ELDERS SAID --

YES, I KNOW.

IT'S BEGUN.

WE NEED TO BRING MY MOM TO A SAFE PLACE.

YES, OF COURSE.

PLEASE FOLLOW ME.

WHERE ARE WE?

THIS IS OUR UNDERGROUND HEADQUARTERS DEEP BELOW THE CITY.

HERE, OUR SECRETS ARE SAFE.

MILTON, PLEASE SHOW THIS GENTLEMAN WHERE TO TAKE THE PATIENT.

YES, BALAN.

YOU SAID THIS PLACE WAS THE HEADQUARTERS. BUT FOR WHAT?

LET ME SHOW YOU.

WELCOME.

TO THE RESISTANCE.

WE'VE GATHERED WARRIORS THE WORLD OVER TO AID IN OUR FIGHT AGAINST THE ELVES.

THEY ARE ALLEDIA'S LAST, BEST HOPE.

OH MY GOSH.

IT'S HIM!

WHOA!

OH BOY, OH BOY.

IT IS AN INCREDIBLE HONOR TO MEET YOU, SIR.

SIR?

WHY ARE THEY CALLING ME THAT?

YOU'LL FIND OUT SOON ENOUGH.

COME. THERE'S SOMEONE WAITING TO MEET YOU.

HE'S AN OLD FRIEND OF YOUR GREAT-GRAND-FATHER SILAS.

AND ONE OF THE FIRST MEMBERS OF THE RESISTANCE.

HIS NAME IS FATHER ADLER.

IS HE A PRIEST?

NOT QUITE.

PLEASE, HAVE A SEAT.

DO YOU KNOW WHY YOU'RE HERE?

WE'RE HERE TO SAVE MY MOM'S LIFE.

OH, BUT YOU WILL DO MUCH MORE THAN THAT.

SO YOU CAN REALLY SEE THE FUTURE?

I HAVE BEEN AROUND FOR SO LONG, AND I'VE SEEN SO MANY THINGS. WHEN YOU LIVE AS LONG AS I DO, YOU BEGIN TO SEE PATTERNS IN LIFE.

WHEN I LOOK INTO THE FUTURE, I AM LOOKING INTO THESE PATTERNS.

YOU CREATURES ARE NOT AS COMPLEX AS YOU MAKE YOURSELVES OUT TO BE.

IF YOU REALLY CAN SEE INTO THE FUTURE, THEN PLEASE TELL ME...

WILL MY SISTER BE OKAY?

IF THERE IS ONLY BAD NEWS TO TELL, DO YOU STILL WISH TO HEAR IT?

IT MIGHT BE BETTER TO SIMPLY HOPE FOR THE BEST.

I NEED TO KNOW THE TRUTH.

WILL SHE BE OKAY?

I SEE THE IMAGE OF YOUR SISTER ARRIVING AT THE SUMMIT OF DEMON'S HEAD MOUNTAIN.

THERE SHE WILL MEET MY BROTHERS, AND SHE WILL ATTEMPT TO PICK THE FRUIT THAT WILL CURE YOUR MOTHER.

THE IMAGES THAT FOLLOW ARE MUCH LESS CLEAR.

BUT ONE PICTURE APPEARS VIVIDLY.

IT IS THE IMAGE OF YOUR SISTER FALLING OFF OF A CLIFF.

SHE IS UNCONSCIOUS, AND DEATH AWAITS HER BELOW.

NO.

MORRIE! WE HAVE TO LEAVE! NOW!

WAIT! YOU'RE SUPPOSED TO HEAR ABOUT YOUR FUTURE!

YES, MY LORD.

I THOUGHT OUR JOB WAS TO CAPTURE HER. NOT KILL HER.

MERCY IS FOR THE WEAK, BOY.

IF SHE WILL NOT JOIN US, THEN KILLING HER IS OUR ONLY OPTION.

SHE IS FAR TOO DANGEROUS TO BE LEFT ALONE.

LUGER, I WOULD LIKE TRELLIS TO BE THE ONE TO DELIVER THE FATAL BLOW.

BY KILLING THE GIRL, HE CAN PROVE HIS LOYALTY TO ME.

SHOULD MY SON FAIL, YOU HAVE MY PERMISSION TO KILL HIM.

IS THAT UNDERSTOOD?

HMM.

SNIF! SNIF!

A FOX.

SIR, MY MEN HAVE REPORTED SEEING THE TARGETS EN ROUTE TO DEMON'S HEAD MOUNTAIN.

LIEUTENANT,

BRING ME THE CRAWLER HOUNDS.

IT IS TIME TO FINISH THIS HUNT.

OTHERWISE, YOU WILL POSE A GREATER THREAT TO OUR SAFETY THAN EVEN OUR ENEMIES.

BUT HER MOTHER GROWS WORSE BY THE HOUR.

WE DON'T HAVE TIME!

THEN WE MUST WORK SWIFTLY.

EMILY, YOU WILL NEED TO CHOOSE A WEAPON.

I CAN OFFER YOU MY SWORD.

WHY DO I NEED A WEAPON?

IT WILL ALLOW YOU TO HARNESS YOUR POWER AND FOCUS YOUR ENERGY.

KEEP YOUR SWORD.

HOW ABOUT THIS WALKING STICK?

VERY WELL.

IT SHOULD BE ADEQUATE FOR OUR PURPOSES.

NOW FOLLOW ME.

SHHK...

LEON.

WHY ARE YOU DOING THIS?

WHY ARE YOU HELPING US?

BECAUSE IN THE END, IT WILL BE YOU HELPING ALL OF US.

I'M ONLY HERE TO SHOW YOU THE WAY.

I DON'T UNDERSTAND.

HOW MUCH DID SILAS TELL YOU ABOUT HIS LIFE'S WORK?

I-I DIDN'T GET A CHANCE TO SPEAK WITH HIM ABOUT IT BEFORE HE PASSED AWAY.

WELL, WHAT HE WOULD HAVE TOLD YOU IS THAT THERE IS A GROUP OF PEOPLE IN ALLEDIA FIGHTING AGAINST THE ELF KING'S TERRIBLE RULE.

SILAS WAS ONE OF THESE PEOPLE.

AND NOW YOU HAVE TAKEN HIS PLACE.

BUT ALL I WANT TO DO IS FIND A CURE FOR MY MOM AND GET MY FAMILY BACK HOME SAFELY.

AND I WILL HELP YOU DO THAT,

BUT THE TRUTH IS THAT YOU HAVE AN EVEN GREATER MISSION AHEAD OF YOU.

YOU MUST UNDERSTAND THAT IF WE DO NOT STOP THE ELF KING, YOUR MOTHER WILL NOT BE THE ONLY ONE TO DIE.

IF WE FAIL, WE WILL ALL PERISH.

BUT WHY ME?

IT'S IN YOUR BLOOD, EMILY.

BUT MY MOM, AND HER FATHER --

THEY'RE DESCENDANTS OF SILAS, TOO.

WHY DIDN'T THEY WEAR THE STONE?

BECAUSE SILAS CHOSE TO LEAVE THEM IN THE DARK.

HE KEPT THEM UNAWARE OF THEIR DUTY AS HEIRS TO THE STONE, AND LEFT THEM TO LEAD WHAT HE FELT WAS A NORMAL LIFE.

WHAT HE FAILED TO REALIZE IS THAT BY KEEPING THEM FROM THEIR FATE,

HE HAS PASSED THEIR BURDEN DOWN TO YOU.

HOW CAN YOU SAY HE FAILED?

HE ONLY DID WHAT HE THOUGHT WAS BEST FOR HIS FAMILY.

94

EVEN WITH YOUR MOTHER'S LIFE ON THE LINE, AND THE LIVES OF HER CHILDREN THREATENED,

YOU WOULD SAY HE DID NOT FAIL?

HAD SILAS CHOSEN TO DO WHAT IS RIGHT FOR ALL OF US, HE COULD HAVE SPARED YOU FROM THIS CURSE.

OR MY MOM COULD HAVE DIED TRYING.

NOT EVERYBODY WANTS TO BE A HERO, LEON.

BUT THEY SHOULD.

NOW LOOK HERE, MISTER REDBEARD.

I KNOW YOU'RE SOME KIND OF GREAT WARRIOR, BUT SILAS LEFT NO MENTION OF YOU.

HE DID, HOWEVER, LEAVE ME TO LOOK AFTER MY MASTER, EMILY.

NOW IF YOU'LL KINDLY SHOW US THE WAY UP THE MOUNTAIN, WE CAN BE ON OUR WAY.

FINE.

IF THAT IS ALL YOU CARE ABOUT, THEN FOLLOW ME.

SEE?

YOU JUST HAVE TO ASK NICELY.

WHAT IS THAT?

IT IS THE ENTRANCE TO THE ONLY KNOWN PASSAGEWAY UP DEMON'S HEAD MOUNTAIN.

YES, BUT WHAT IS THAT BLOCKING THE WAY?

TWENTY TONS OF EXPLOSIVES.

IF ANYONE WERE TO TRY AND IGNITE IT, THE EXPLOSION WOULD DESTROY THE ENTRANCE.

AND THE INTRUDERS.

IT IS MEANT TO BE A SAFEGUARD TO KEEP PEOPLE AWAY FROM THIS PLACE.

LEON, I CAN'T DO IT.

YES, YOU CAN.

TRY AGAIN.

BUT THIS TIME, TRY USING YOUR STAFF.

HOW WILL THIS HELP?

TOK!

INFUSE THE STAFF WITH THE POWER OF THE STONE.

IT WILL HELP YOU FOCUS THE ENERGY.

BUT I'LL BURN IT, LIKE THE SEEDS.

MISS EMILY,

YOU'VE BEEN ABLE TO DO THIS BEFORE.

YOU LIFTED ME WITHOUT BURNING ME, REMEMBER?

YOU SEE?

YOU ALREADY KNOW HOW TO DO THIS.

BUT WITH MISKIT, IT'S DIFFERENT.

HOW SO?

I-I DON'T KNOW. IT JUST IS.

AND WHY DO YOU THINK THAT IS?

BECAUSE! I DON'T WANT TO HURT HIM, I WANT TO PROTECT HIM.

HE'S A LIVING THING.

WELL, SO IS THIS SEED.

NOW PROTECT IT.

IT'S NOT THE SAME.

BUT IT IS.

SOON, YOU'LL COME TO UNDERSTAND THAT EVERYTHING HAS A LIFE FORCE...

SOME LIVES ARE EASY TO DETECT.

KSHING!

BUT TO FIND OTHERS, YOU HAVE TO LOOK BENEATH THE SURFACE.

LISTEN FOR YOUR STAFF'S LIFE FORCE AND FOCUS YOUR ENERGY ON IT.

TREAT IT LIKE A PART OF YOU.

NOW TRY PICKING UP THE SEED.

TREAT IT THE SAME WAY.

FOCUS.

WELL DONE.

LET'S TRY SOMETHING A LITTLE BIGGER.

CATCH!

WELCOME BACK, YOUNG MASTER.

I WAS BEGINNING TO THINK YOU WERE UPSET WITH ME.

KRA-KOOM!!

EMILY?

YOU DON'T NEED THEM, MASTER. WE CAN DO THIS ON OUR OWN.

ARE YOU OKAY?

THEY'LL ONLY SLOW US DOWN AND MAKE US WEAKER.

LEAVE THEM BEHIND.

THIS ROAD BELONGS TO US.

YOU'RE GROWING IN STRENGTH.

AND SO IS THE STONE.

THE MORE POWERFUL THE AMULET BECOMES, THE MORE DIFFICULT IT WILL BE TO CONTROL.

AND WHAT HAPPENS IF I LOSE CONTROL?

THEN WE WOULD BE IN A WHOLE HEAP OF TROUBLE.

BUT IT WON'T HAPPEN.

HOW DO YOU KNOW?

BECAUSE I BELIEVE THE GADOBA TREES WERE RIGHT ABOUT YOU.

THE GADOBA TREES?

YOU CAN SPEAK TO THEM?

OF COURSE.

AND I IMAGINE THEY LOOK FORWARD TO SPEAKING WITH YOU, TOO.

NOW, FOLLOW ME.

WE DON'T HAVE TIME TO LOSE.

THEY ONLY HAVE A FEW FOOT SOLDIERS PATROLLING.

IT'S NOW OR NEVER!

OKAY, GUYS. HERE WE GO.

MILO'S RUBBISH

WHERE DO YOU THINK YOU'RE GOING?

THIS DOCK IS OFF-LIMITS.

I WAS TOLD BY THE COMMANDER TO EMPTY THE GARBAGE BEFORE PRESENTING THE HOUSE TO THE KING.

IF YOU WANT TO HANDLE IT, BE MY GUEST!

OPEN IT UP.

YOU SURE YOU WANT TO DO THAT?

I SAID OPEN IT!

DON'T SAY I DIDN'T WARN YA.

OH, THAT'S RIGHT.

ELVES CAN'T STAND THE SMELL OF FISH, CAN THEY?

THE LAST PICKUP WAS THE MARINA.

SORRY.

GAK!

HMM.

I SUPPOSE THAT'S WHY WE GET TO HAVE THESE JOBS.

LUCKY US.

GO! JUST HURRY AND GO!!

GAK!

HACK! COUGH!

HEH, HEH.

OKAY, BOYS, YOU'RE UP.

HMM.

YOU FIRST.

SHLP! SHLP!

UGH!

TRASH

OOF!

WE NEED TO GET TO THE ATTIC.

THERE THEY ARE.

YOU HAVE THE KEY?

RIGHT HERE.

MORRIE SAID ALL I HAVE TO DO IS PLUG THIS INTO THE MAIN TERMINAL.

JUST GOTTA FIND IT.

BOOT SEQUENCE INITIATED.

WE SHOULD BE UP AND RUNNING IN THIRTY MINUTES.

COGSLEY, DO YOU BELIEVE IN PREMONITIONS?

THAT'S A STRANGE QUESTION TO ASK A ROBOT,

BUT I DO BELIEVE IN PREDICTIONS BASED ON SOUND MATHEMATICAL ASSUMPTIONS.

IF THE "PREMONITIONS" WERE BASED ON SUCH MATH, I WOULD BELIEVE THEM.

THEN LET'S HOPE TREES ARE BAD AT MATH.

PSHT!

NGH.

WHY AREN'T YOU USING THE STONE?

I CAN DO THIS WITHOUT THE STONE!

NOT NEARLY AS FAST.

YOU'RE GOING TO KILL YOURSELF.

WE BETTER REST HERE FOR NOW.

YOU NEVER ANSWERED MY QUESTION, LEON.

WHAT HAPPENS TO A STONEKEEPER WHEN THEY LOSE CONTROL OF THE STONE?

THEY... ...CHANGE.

CHANGE?

THIRTY YEARS AGO, A GROUP OF FOUR YOUNG STONEKEEPERS LOST CONTROL OF THEIR POWERS...

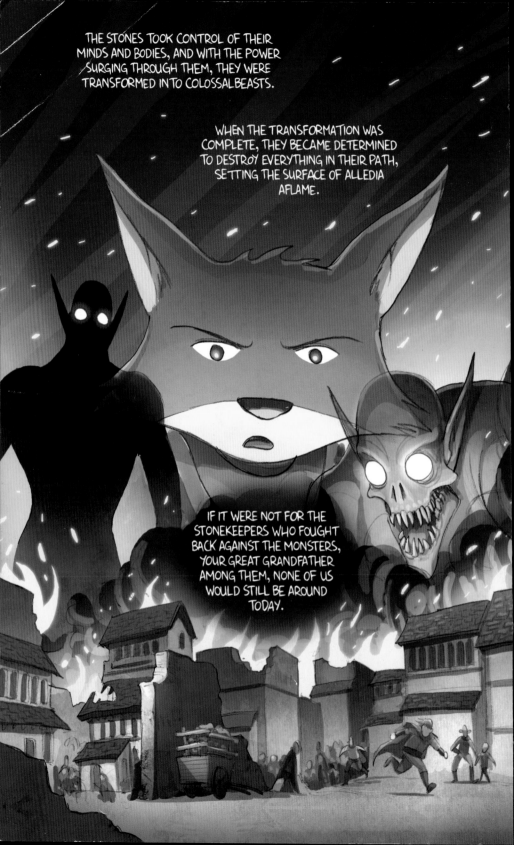

THE RESISTANCE WAS
ABLE TO DESTROY THESE
POWER-HUNGRY ROGUE
STONEKEEPERS.

EXCEPT FOR ONE.

HE USED TO BE A QUIET
BOY FROM A SMALL ELF
VILLAGE, BUT AFTER HIS
TRANSFORMATION, HE
WAS NEVER THE SAME.

THE ELDERS WERE ABLE
TO SEPARATE HIM FROM
HIS STONE, AND DESPITE
HIS REQUESTS TO BE
EXECUTED, THEY LOCKED
HIM UP IN AN ATTEMPT
TO CURE HIM OF ITS
CURSE.

BUT WHEN HE TALKED,
HE SPOKE ONLY OF HIS
DESIRE FOR POWER, AND
WARNED OF DARK DAYS
TO COME.

HE TOLD THEM THAT
THEY WOULD REGRET
HAVING KEPT HIM
ALIVE,

AND THAT
HE WOULD SHOW
THEM WHY.

SO THAT BOY WAS THE ELF KING.

YES.

IS THAT WHY YOU'RE DOING THIS? BECAUSE HE KILLED YOUR FATHER?

I AM NOT MOTIVATED BY VENGEANCE.

I DO THIS TO HONOR HIM.

THESE STONES ARE WHAT KILLED YOUR FATHER.

SO HOW CAN YOU TRUST ME?

MY MISSION HAS ALWAYS BEEN TO DESTROY THE ELF KING.

AND YOU'RE THE BEST HOPE I HAVE FOR SEEING THAT HAPPEN.

WHAT ARE YOU HIDING, TRELLIS?

HIDING?

I CAN SENSE YOUR HESITATION.

THE AIR AROUND YOU IS AS THICK AS BLOOD.

NGH...

SOME DAY YOU MAY ALSO LEARN TO DO WHAT IS RIGHT,

EVEN IF IT HURTS.

I'M SORRY, MY PRINCE.

BUT I WILL NOT LET YOU RUIN MY OPPORTUNITY.

LET'S MOVE.

THE GADOBA FOREST SHOULD BE AROUND HERE SOMEWHERE.

I DON'T SEE ANYTHING.

THE FOG IS TOO THICK.

THAT'S STRANGE.

SHOULDN'T THOSE TREES BE RIGHT --

I--

BROTHER MALKEN!

I SENSE SOMETHING DIFFERENT ABOUT THIS ONE.

DON'T YOU?

YES... YES...

DIFFERENT INDEED.

WHY DID ALL THESE PEOPLE DIE?

BECAUSE THEY PICKED THE WRONG FRUIT, OF COURSE.

FOR EVERY ONE FRUIT THAT GIVES LIFE, THERE ARE A HUNDRED THAT TAKE IT AWAY.

VERY FEW SUCCEED IN FINDING THEIR PRIZE.

LEON REDBEARD.

IT HAS BEEN A LONG TIME, MY FRIEND.

I PROMISED THAT I WOULD RETURN.

YES.

AND NOW YOU BELIEVE THIS GIRL TO BE THE ONE WE'RE LOOKING FOR?

I AM CERTAIN OF IT.

VERY WELL.

SHOW US.

EMILY, CHOOSE A FRUIT, AND EAT IT.

BUT HOW DO I CHOOSE THE RIGHT ONE?

JUST REMEMBER WHAT I TOLD YOU.

EVERYTHING HAS A LIFE FORCE.

NONE OF THESE.

THIS...

THIS IS THE ONE.

EMILY, WAIT!

SQUISH!!

UGH!

EMILY!

I'M FINE.

IT JUST TASTES TERRIBLE.

LEON IS RIGHT.

YOU DO HAVE THE GIFT.

THERE IS MORE WHERE THAT CAME FROM.

PLEASE FEEL FREE TO HARVEST THEM.

LEON, IS THIS ENOUGH TO CURE MY MOTHER?

YES.

THEN THIS IS ALL WE NEED.

THANK YOU FOR YOUR HELP.

NO.

THANK YOU, YOUNG STONEKEEPER.

AND GOOD LUCK.

WHAT ARE YOU DOING?

WE SHOULD TAKE AS MANY AS WE CAN!

WHAT IF WE LOSE THAT ONE?

AND JUST IMAGINE WHAT WE COULD DO WITH MORE!

IF WE TAKE MORE THAN WE NEED, WE'RE BOUND TO CAUSE MORE TROUBLE.

I TOLD YOU I'M HERE TO SAVE MY MOM.

THAT'S IT.

BUT...

BUT...

AT LEAST GET A FRESH ONE!

SH!

WHAT IS IT?

I SAW SOMETHING MOVING OUT THERE.

WE NEED TO LEAVE NOW.

I'M SORRY, FATHER MALKEN.

IT'S LIKELY THAT ELVES ARE ON OUR TRAIL.

WE WERE CARELESS.

DO NOT WORRY ABOUT US, LEON.

LEAVE QUICKLY AND KEEP THE STONEKEEPER SAFE.

IT WILL BE UP TO YOU TO SEE THAT SHE REACHES HER FULL POTENTIAL.

AND BE CAREFUL --

YOUR JOURNEY DOWN THE MOUNTAIN WILL BE FAR MORE TREACHEROUS THAN THE JOURNEY HERE.

OH, AND PLEASE GIVE BROTHER ADLER OUR WELL WISHES.

I WILL.

LET'S GO.

WE'LL BE HARDER TO TRACK IN THE NIGHT.

BROTHER MALKEN,

WHY DID YOU NOT TELL HIM ABOUT WHAT LIES AHEAD?

HE ALREADY KNOWS.

WHAT'S WRONG?

DID YOU SEE SOMETHING?

NO. IT'S NOTHING.

KRAK!

EMILY!

CRUMBLE!

LATCH!

REGARDLESS, I CANNOT LET SUCH CRIMES GO UNPUNISHED,

NOW CAN I?

BURN THEM DOWN. ALL OF THEM.

YES, SIR.

BROTHER MALKEN, IS THIS THE END?

WE ARE NOT THE LAST OF THE GADOBA, BROTHER HENN.

SO LET US HOPE THIS IS ONLY A NEW BEGINNING.

THE FOREST IS BURNING.

HEY --

THE ELVES WERE RIGHT BEHIND US.

WE HAVE TO GO BACK.

NO.

THERE'S NOTHING WE CAN DO TO HELP.

THE ELVES ARE CLOSE, SO WE MUST HURRY.

LET'S GO.

EMILY,

DON'T YOU SEE THE TROUBLE YOU ARE CAUSING FOR OTHERS?

WE CAN END ALL OF THEIR SUFFERING NOW.

YOU CAN-NOT RELY ON THEM --

FOR THEIR SAKE.

YOU MUST TAKE MATTERS INTO YOUR OWN HANDS!

YOU AND I CAN DESTROY THE ELVES OURSELVES.

JUST LET THE STONE TAKE CONTROL.

NO.

I NEED TO BELIEVE IN MY FRIENDS AND FAMILY.

WHY?

BECAUSE YOU SEE THAT THEY ARE VALUABLE IN YOUR QUEST FOR POWER?

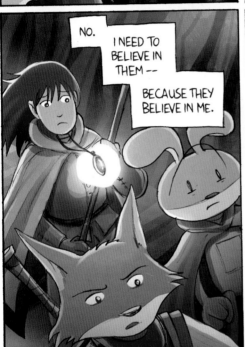
NO.

I NEED TO BELIEVE IN THEM --

BECAUSE THEY BELIEVE IN ME.

AND HOW WILL YOU FEEL WHEN THEY ALL DIE FOR YOU?

THAT WON'T HAPPEN.

HOW CAN YOU BE SO SURE?

BECAUSE I WON'T LET IT HAPPEN.

SNAP!

DID YOU HEAR THAT?

REMEMBER, RETAIN CONTROL OF YOUR POWER.

THE MORE ENERGY YOU USE, THE STRONGER THE STONE BECOMES.

YOU MUST NOT LET IT TAKE OVER.

I WON'T.

KILL THEM.

HWEEEEE...

KRAK!

THOOM!

HE IS MUCH TOO POWERFUL.

IN KNOWLEDGE AND SKILL YOU ARE OUTMATCHED.

THERE IS ONLY ONE WAY FOR YOU TO DEFEAT HIM.

YOU MUST GIVE CONTROL TO THE STONE.

AAAAH!

KRAK!

AGH!

EMILY!

SZRAK!

SZT!!!

GIVE IN TO THE STONE!

LET IT TAKE AWAY YOUR PAIN!

SZRAK! KRNCH!

UNH!

KTANG!

PAF!!!

EMILY, GET UP! GET UP NOW!

ACCEPT THE STONE'S FULL POWER BEFORE IT'S TOO LATE!

I'M THE ONE IN CONTROL!

AND YOU WILL DIE HOLDING ON TO IT!

LET THE STONE TAKE OVER AND MAKE YOUR TRANSFORMATION COMPLETE!

GOOD-BYE, YOUNG STONEKEEPER.

I WOULD HAVE PREFERRED A SPIRITED BATTLE, BUT AN EXECUTION WILL DO.

SHIVER SHIVER

AGH!

SLRAK!!

LITTLE WORM, WHAT DO YOU THINK YOU'RE DOING?!

WHAT MAKES YOU THINK YOU CAN DEFEAT ME?

BECAUSE THE KING TAUGHT ME EVERYTHING HE TAUGHT YOU.

NO.

NOT EVERYTHING.

HA HA HA HA HA

RRRGH!

EMILY, GET UP.

I-I CAN'T.

THE STONE -- IT'S TRYING TO TAKE OVER.

YOU NEED TO REGAIN CONTROL.

WITHOUT YOUR HELP, WE WON'T MAKE IT OUT OF THIS ALIVE.

GROWR!

THOOM!

EM!!!

WILL SHE BE ALL RIGHT?

SHE IS BATTLING TO CONTROL THE POWER OF THE STONE.

THE STONE'S INFLUENCE IS STRONG,

BUT SHE WILL SUCCEED.

SHE JUST NEEDS A LITTLE MORE TIME.

THEN WE'LL GIVE HER SOME.

STRAP EVERYONE IN.

SHIVER SHIVER

NAVIN, THIS HOUSE WAS NOT BUILT FOR BATTLE.

WE'RE JUST GOING TO STALL.

177

TOSS!

THOOM!

AHH!

ALL SYSTEMS ARE DOWN!

WE'RE DEAD IN THE WATER!

NO.

I CAN DEFEAT IT WITHOUT LOSING CONTROL.

BUT HOW CAN YOU FIGHT SUCH A MONSTER WITHOUT BECOMING ONE YOURSELF?

BY NOT FIGHTING ALONE.

NAVIN...

EM!

GET BACK IN THE DRIVER'S SEAT.

I'M GOING TO NEED YOUR HELP.

BUT... THE HOUSE IS DESTROYED.

WHAT DO YOU INTEND TO DO?

IT'S LIKE YOU SAID, LEON.

EVERYTHING HAS A LIFE FORCE.

WHAT'S HAPPENING NOW?

I DON'T KNOW, BUT STAY IN THAT SEAT.

SIZZLE

SZRAK!

WELL, LOOK AT THAT.

ALL SYSTEMS ARE BACK ONLINE.

I'M GOING TO NEED SOME OF THE AUXILIARY POWER TO PUSH US BACK UP.

YOU READY?

PUNCH IT, COGSLEY!

KSHT!

MORE POWER, EM!!!

EM?

EM!!

UNNHN...

SIZZLE SIZZLE!

MOM?

EMILY.

IF THIS IS A DREAM, I DON'T WANT TO WAKE UP.

THIS ISN'T A DREAM, SWEETIE.

EVERYTHING'S GOING TO BE ALL RIGHT.

WE'RE GOING HOME NOW.

NO, MOM.

ONLY YOU AND NAVIN ARE GOING HOME.

I HAVE TO STAY HERE.

EVEN IF I TRIED TO LEAVE,

I THINK SOMETHING WOULD STOP ME.

THEN I'LL STAY HERE UNTIL WE CAN ALL GO HOME TOGETHER.

BUT YOU CAN'T STAY HERE!

YOU DON'T KNOW WHAT WE'RE UP AGAINST.

IT'S TOO DANGEROUS FOR YOU TO BE HERE!

I'M NOT GOING TO JUST LEAVE YOU ON YOUR OWN, EMILY!

FRANKLY, I DON'T CARE WHAT WE'RE UP AGAINST.

I'M STICKING WITH YOU.

BUT, MOM, I'M BEING SERIOUS.

SO AM I.

MY HOME IS WHEREVER YOU AND NAVIN ARE.

I APPRECIATE YOUR CONCERN,

BUT REMEMBER I'M STILL *YOUR* MOTHER.

WE'RE GOING TO WORK THROUGH THIS TOGETHER,

OKAY?

OKAY.

NOW PLEASE EXPLAIN TO ME HOW THE HECK WE GOT HERE.

NAVIN SAYS THIS IS ALL YOUR FAULT.

SHE'S AWAKE!

EM!

NAVIN!

YOU DID GOOD.

YOU BOTH PERFORMED ADMIRABLY.

YOUR MOTHER SHOULD BE VERY PROUD.

SO WE WON?

FOR NOW.

BUT THIS IS ONLY THE BEGINNING.

THE ELVES WILL NOW COME AFTER US WITH THE FULL STRENGTH OF THEIR ARMY.

WE'LL BE READY.

YES, BUT IN ORDER TO BE READY, WE WILL NEED TO WORK HARD AND PREPARE.

YOUR TRAINING BEGINS TOMORROW, SO GET SOME REST.

LOOKS LIKE YOU ALL HAVE SOME CATCHING UP TO DO.

I'LL LEAVE YOU BE.

THANK YOU, LEON.

FOR EVERYTHING.

GET SOME REST.

HE SEEMS LIKE A REALLY NICE --

-- ANIMAL PERSON.

213

YOU GUYS DEFINITELY MADE SOME VERY INTERESTING FRIENDS WHILE I WAS AWAY.

MASTER EMILY!

MISKIT!

YOUR ARM! ARE YOU HURT?

OH, THIS IS NOTHING. IT SHOULD REPAIR ITSELF IN A DAY OR SO.

THANK YOU SO MUCH FOR LOOKING OUT FOR ME.

IT'S WHAT I WAS BUILT TO DO.

WELL, YOU'RE DOING A GREAT JOB.

WE JUST GOT THE MAIN ENGINE BACK ONLINE, CHIEF.

WE'LL BE OPERATIONAL BY THE END OF THE DAY.

NICE WORK, COGSLEY.

I'LL SEE YOU BACK IN THE CONTROL ROOM.

I GOTTA GO WASH MY HEAD.

MY GOODNESS, YOU GUYS SOUND SO... GROWN-UP.

I'M VERY IMPRESSED.

SO THIS IS OUR NEW HOME.

END OF BOOK TWO

WRITTEN AND DRAWN BY

KAZU KIBUISHI

COLORS AND BACKGROUNDS BY

KAZU KIBUISHI
AMY KIM KIBUISHI
ANTHONY GO WU
JASON CAFFOE

COLOR FLATTING ASSISTANCE BY

KEAN SOO
STUART LIVINGSTON
DENVER JACKSON
RYAN HOFFMANN
MICHAEL REGINA
TIM DURNING
CATHERINE YOO
ALAN BEADLE
PATRICK RACE
CAYLEIGH ALLEN
FELIX LIM